Girl Arranging Her Hair

by Kirsten Anderson
illustrated by Jeremy Tugeau

Table of Contents

Chapter 1

A Model

Louise said, "Madame Cassatt asked for me?"

Louise's mother said, "Yes. She wants you to be her model for a painting. Will you do it?"

Louise was surprised. Why would an artist want to paint her? She was not beautiful.

Her mother said, "You know Madame Cassatt. She is the American artist."

Louise said, "I will do it."

The next morning Louise and her sisters Claudia and Annette talked about the painting.

Claudia said, "You will wear a costume."

Annette said, "Maybe you will be a princess."

Louise liked to look at the paintings in art shops. The people in the paintings looked beautiful and real.

Annette said, "Louise will be famous!"

Louise and her sisters liked to look at the paintings in art shops.

Chapter 2

Staying Still

Madame Cassatt said, "Good morning, Louise. Please come in."

Louise walked into Madame Cassatt's art room.

There were many paintings in Madame Cassatt's art room.

Madame Cassatt said, "I want to begin working now. I like to use the daylight. And please, call me Mary."

Louise said, "Yes, Mary."

🎧 Mary gave Louise a brush.

Louise hoped to wear a costume. But Mary asked her to sit at a table.

Mary said, "Brush your hair."

Mary gave Louise a brush. Louise brushed her hair. Mary watched her. Louise felt strange.

Mary asked Louise to try arranging her hair. Louise began arranging her hair in different ways.

Mary said, "That's perfect! Now stay very still."

Mary began to draw. Louise stayed still. She did not move. It was hard work. Later it was time to go home. Louise was happy.

 **Clue**: You can use context clues to help you understand the meaning of a word. Can you understand what arranging means by using the context clues in the paragraph?

Chapter 3

The Painting

It was hard to stay still for so long. Louise was tired. And there were no costumes! Louise thought, "A painting of someone arranging her hair is not interesting."

After a few days, Louise became good at staying still. She talked to Mary. The time went by faster. Mary told Louise about her home in the United States.

Mary also told Louise about how she became an artist. She traveled to France, Spain, and Italy to study the great paintings of the world. Later Mary tried to find her own way of painting.

Finally the painting was finished. Mary showed Louise the painting.

Louise looked at the painting. She wanted to cry. But she told Mary that the painting was nice.

Clue: France is a proper noun. A proper noun names a person, place, or event. Proper nouns always begin with a capital letter. Can you find more proper nouns on this page?

Chapter 4

A New Look

Louise did not like the painting. It did not look real. Louise did not look beautiful. She tried to forget the painting.

In the spring, Louise got a note from Mary. The painting was going to be in an art show.

Louise went to the art show. She saw many paintings. Then she saw Mary's painting. The lights made the painting look different. Louise was not beautiful in the painting. But she looked like she was thinking. She looked interesting.

Louise thought, "It's just me. I like it."

⟳ Louise saw Mary's painting at the art show.

Comprehension Check

Summarize the Story

Use a Character Web to write words that describe Louise. Then use information from the web to summarize the story.

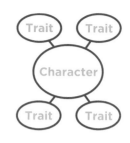

Think and Compare

1. Did Louise like the painting at first? Why or why not? *(Analyze Character)*

2. Would you like to be a model for a painting? What is one bad thing about being a model? *(Apply)*

3. Do you think paintings need to look real? Why or why not? *(Evaluate)*